My P

Written by Gill Hamlyn
Illustrated by Steve Smallman

I wanted a spider.

I wanted a frog.

I wanted a snake.

I wanted a dog.

I wanted a parrot.

I wanted a bat.

8

I wanted a monkey.

I got a cat!

I wanted a spider.
I wanted a frog.
I wanted a snake.
I wanted a dog.
I wanted a parrot.
I wanted a bat.
I wanted a monkey.
I got a cat!